For Destiny and Kiyoko.
~C.M.

Believe that you can, and you will achieve anything.
~A.L.

ISLAND HERITAGE™
PUBLISHING
A DIVISION OF THE MADDEN CORPORATION

94-411 Kōʻaki Street
Waipahu, Hawaiʻi 96797-2806
Orders: (800) 468-2800
Information: (808) 564-8800
Fax: (808) 564-8877
welcometotheislands.com

ISBN: 1-61710-362-4
First Edition, First Printing—2017
COP 171606

Kona
and His Hard Shell

Written by Crissy Miyake • Illustrated by Anneth Lagamo

ISLAND HERITAGE™
PUBLISHING

Kona is a young crab growing up in the
warm waters off the Big Island of Hawai'i.

Kona spends most days playing.
He loves to climb *limu*, hide in the
sand, and chase his friends in the reef.

One day while playing, Kona noticed the water
getting rougher and the sky getting dark.
The waves were getting so big and strong.

It was a hurricane!

Kona tried to hide in the sand but a big wave pulled him out. He tossed around and hit a piece of coral. *Auwe!* Kona was hurt!

Kona was scared. He hid under some coral until the storm passed. When it was all over, Kona saw that he had a small *puka* in his shell. He went home and his mama patched up his shell with a special *'opihi* to cover up his *puka*.

After a while, the *puka* on Kona's shell got smaller and his mama took off the *'opihi*. All that was left was a thick heart shaped bump on his shell.

Kona liked the heart on his shell and he felt better but…it reminded him of when he got hurt and sometimes he would still get scared, like when the waters got rough or the sky got dark. Sometimes Kona even had bad dreams about the hurricane.

One morning, Kona woke up from a bad dream and he decided he would tell his mama about it. Mama listened and said, "Sometimes after something really scary happens, something you see, hear, or feel reminds you about the scary thing."

Then mama asked Kona if he wanted to learn some tricks to help him remember he was safe when he got scared. "You mean even when I'm outside playing?" Kona asked.

"Yes, my Kona crab, even when you are outside." Mama replied. "If you get scared, these tricks could help." Kona sat down next to mama and listened closely.

First mama said, "Take a big deep breath in through your nose and fill your *'opu* with air." Slowly, Kona took a deep breath in through his nose. Mama counted aloud "1—2—3—4— 5—." Then mama said, "Blow out the air slowly through your mouth, like when you want to blow a really big bubble that won't pop." Kona blew the air out slowly while Mama counted again, "1—2—3—4— 5—." Kona blew a perfectly huge bubble and watched as the bubble floated away.

Mama asked Kona how he was feeling. Kona paused, thought about it, and said, "I feel a little better, but I'm still kind of thinking about scary things."

"Okay Kona, let's keep breathing in and out slowly until your body feels more relaxed and your thoughts are more calm."

Kona slowly took a deep breath in 1—2—3—4—5— and he slowly breathed out 1—2—3—4—5—. Then Kona said, "I still have some scary thoughts, but it's slowing down and my body feels calmer."

Mama smiled and said, "Good job Kona. Now you are ready to do the next part."

Mama said, "Name five colors you see." Kona looked around him and he saw a big green *honu*, a pink sea star, some white coral, a black eel, and a yellow sea snail. As Kona looked around he remembered how much he loved his reef home and all the sea creatures who were his friends.

Kona smiled when he
remembered some of the happy
times, like when he played hide
and seek by the white coral.

Then mama said, "Name four things you can hear." Kona listened hard. He heard waves above him, dolphins swimming, a whale singing far away, and bubbles popping. Kona listened to the whale's song as it got further and further away and he felt himself start to get more relaxed.

Then mama said, "Name three things you can touch." Kona calmed down even more as he paid attention to his body and felt the warm water on his shell, the sand under his claws, and a hard piece of lava rock under him.

Then mama said, "Name two things you smell." Kona had to try really hard but he smelled saltiness and seaweed. The smell reminded him how much fun he has climbing *limu*.

Then mama said, "Name one special thing about yourself." Kona closed his eyes and thought and thought.

Kona could feel his heart beating strong, **ba—bump, ba—bump, ba—bump** and he remembered the heart on his shell.

He opened his eyes wide and said,
"I'm a strong crab with a special
heart on my shell!"

Mama hugged Kona and said, "Yes my Kona, you have a
strong heart on the inside and now the outside too!"
Kona smiled as his mama hugged him. He felt better.
His body was relaxed and his mind was calm.

Kona wasn't thinking about scary things anymore and he
felt strong and safe knowing that if he got scared again,
he had a trick that would work no matter where he was.

Mama kissed Kona on his special heart on his
shell and he went outside to play with his friends.

The End

Glossary:

Auwe [ahh-way] - expression, Oh no!

Honu [ho-new] - sea turtle

Limu [LEE-moo] - seaweed

'Opihi [OH- pee-hee] - an umbrella shaped edible limpet that grows on rocks in Hawai'i

'Opu [oh-Pooh] - belly, stomach

Puka [POOH-kah] - a hole, opening

A Note for parents/adults on trauma and grounding:

Trauma is when a child experiences an event or events that cause feelings of horror, helplessness, and/or loss of control. The child may perceive him/herself or others are in danger. They may even believe that death is likely/possible. This type of experience creates feelings of vulnerability and a loss of safety and control. Some examples include; physical abuse, sexual abuse, exposure to community violence (shooting, mugging, burglary), witnessing domestic Violence, experiencing a serious illness, injury, or medical procedure, natural disasters, etc.

Grounding is a technique to stay present in the moment and to practice connecting the body to the here and now. This skill is especially important with trauma because often times even though events may have happened in the past, memories can make it feel like they are happening again in the present. The physical body holds memory and recalls its experience (e.g., muscles tighten, a freeze response, etc.). When re-experiencing physical sensations happen in response to a memory or trigger, it helps to "ground" back to the safety of the present moment. Grounding skills help a child learn how to manage overwhelming trauma-related emotions and triggers. It fosters a sense of empowerment so that instead of feeling powerless and re-traumatized, they take back control of their body and feel powerful. Grounding exercises like the one in the story, often takes the form of focusing on the present by tuning in more consciously to the immediate environment.

Deep Breathing is another technique that helps to ground the physical body to the here and now and relax. Sometimes when feeling anxious or threatened, the body responds by speeding up breathing. Breaths can shorten and quicken as the body gets ready to respond to danger. By practicing deep breathing and slowing down each breath, the body will respond in kind and know it is safe to relax.